Scamp is collecting conkers

Join each tree to the correct number.

1
2
3
4
5

Write the numbers.

Scamp visits the pet shop.

How many puppies are there?
Colour the puppies and the number.

Count, then write
the number.

Make 6 biscuits in each bag for Scamp.

Pre-School **Nursery Numbers Book 3**

Schofield & Sims

NURSERY NUMBERS 3

Name

Scamp meets a robot.

Can you recognise these shapes?

Colour △ blue ○ red □ yellow ▭ green

Can you continue this pattern?

Scamp is waiting for a bus.

How many dogs are waiting?

Count, then write the number.

Make 7 dogs.

Where do you think they are going?

5

Scamp in the rain

Count and colour the umbrellas.

Count the puddles and raindrops. Write the numbers.

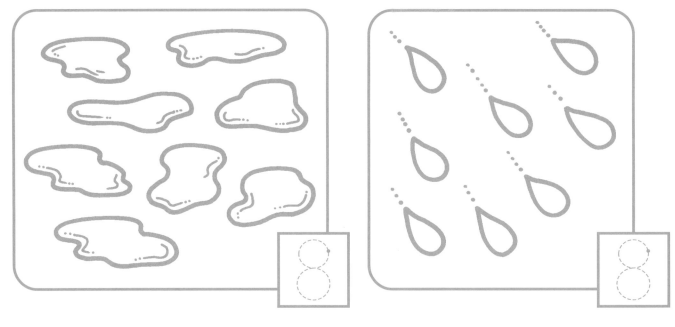

Make 8 wellies.

Scamp enjoys the sun.

Count and colour the suns.

Count and write the numbers.

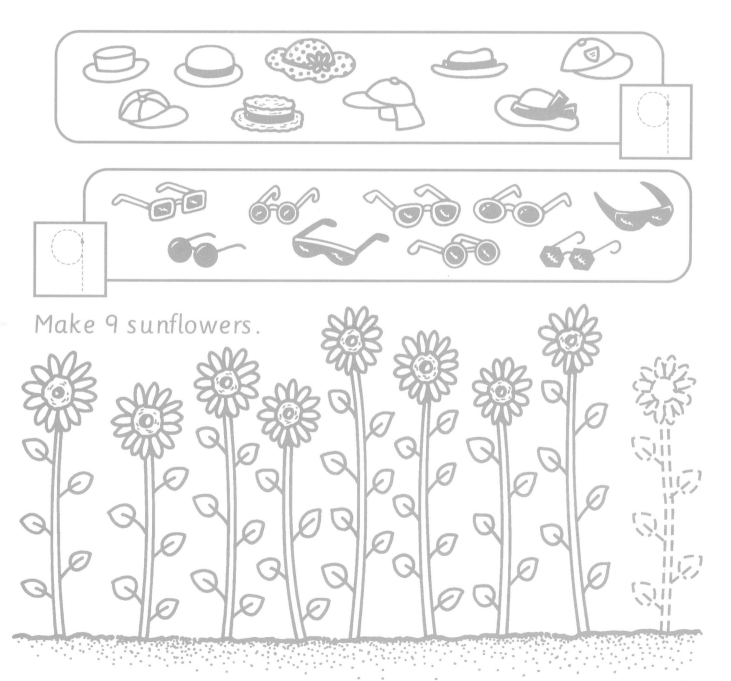

Make 9 sunflowers.

Scamp in the snow

Count the snowballs.

Count the snowflakes and skates. Write the number.

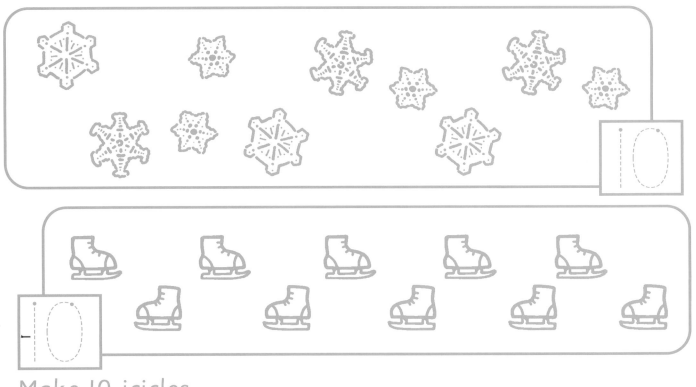

Make 10 icicles.

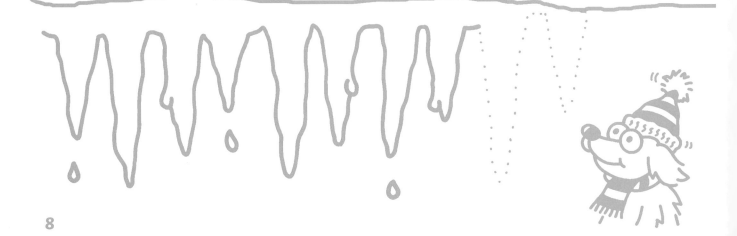

8

Writing numbers.

6 6 6 6 6 6
7 7 7 7 7 7
8 8 8 8 8 8
9 9 9 9 9 9
10 10 10 10 10 10

Scamp went to the butchers to buy lots of sausages.
Match the links of sausages to the correct number.

6
7
8
9
10

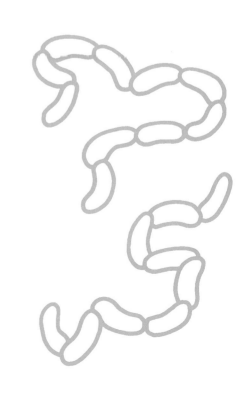

Bonfire Night

Count and write the number.

Scamp doesn't like loud bangs, do you?
Please keep pets inside on Bonfire Night.

Colour the correct number on each line.

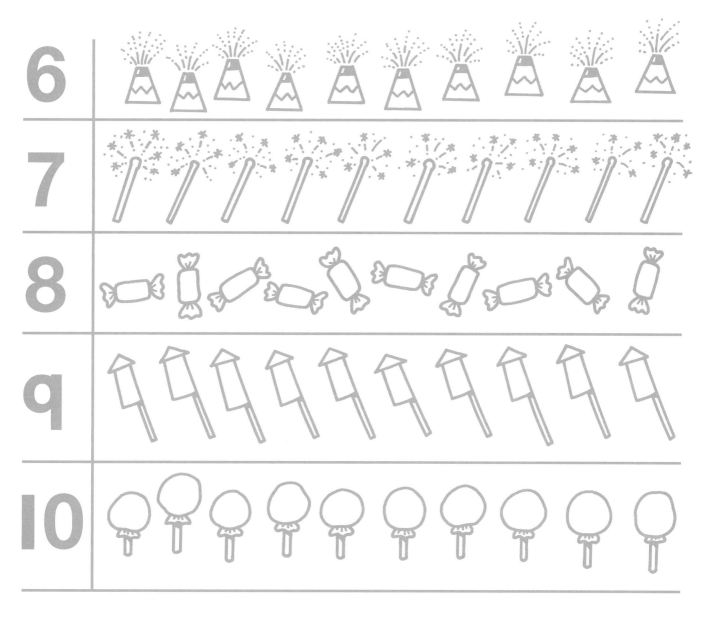

Write the numbers.

Never touch or go near fireworks.

Where is Scamp?
Join the dots to find out.
What shapes have you made?

Draw the next thing in these patterns.

Scamp is feeding the birds.

You can help him.

Draw the correct number.

Is there enough bread?

Colour 6 on each line.

Scamp enjoys the garden.
He needs your help. Draw the correct number.

Colour 7 things on each line.

Scamp wants an ice-cream.

Help him to decide which one to choose.
Draw the correct number.

Colour 8 things on each line.

Scamp has picked some flowers.

Draw the correct number.

Colour 9 in each row.

Scamp is making vegetable soup.
Help him to prepare it.
Draw the correct number.

Colour 10 in each line.

Scamp visits the Sea Life Centre.
Look and count.

How many does Scamp see?

What else did Scamp see?

Join the dots to find out.

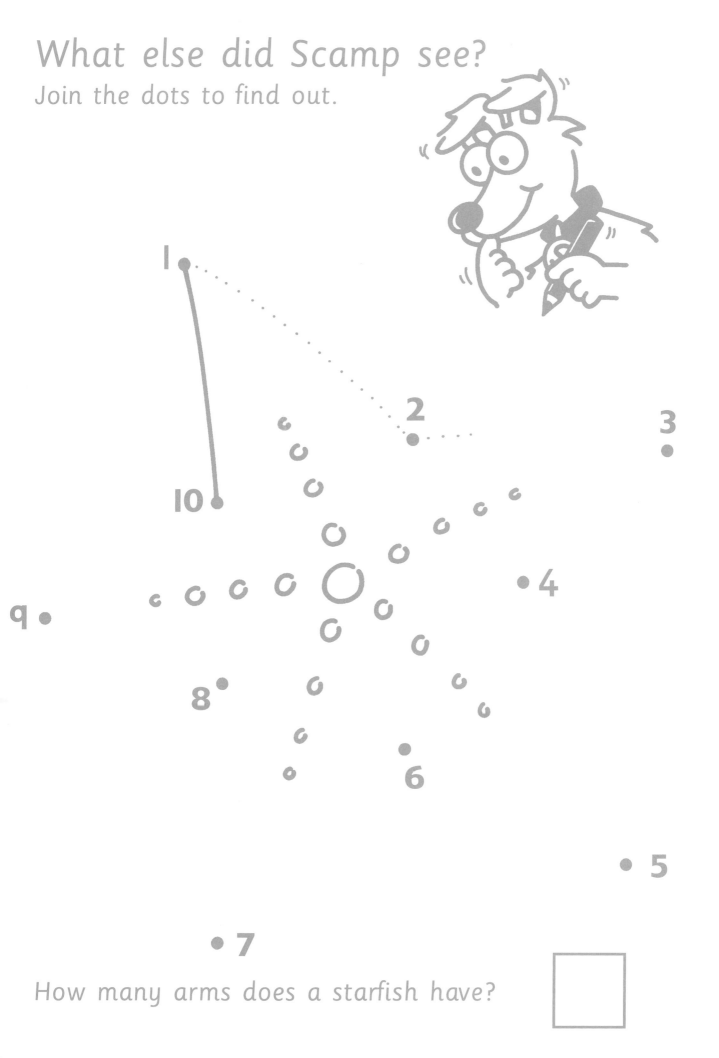

How many arms does a starfish have?

Scamp is in the garden.

What can Scamp see? Count and write the number.

Scamp is in the supermarket.

Count and ring the correct number in each row.

Make each shelf have the
same number as this one.

Inside

Colour the animals that are inside.

Draw yourself
inside the house.

Outside

Colour the animals that are outside.

Draw Scamp's ball outside the goal posts.

Schofield & Sims
HELPING CHILDREN TO LEARN

Schofield & Sims was established in 1901 by two headmasters and since then our name has been synonymous with educationally sound texts and teaching materials. Our mission is to publish products which are:

- Educationally sound • Good value • Written by experienced teachers
- Extensively used in schools, nurseries and play groups
- Used by parents to support their children's learning

NURSERY NUMBERS BOOK 3

Six books which comprise a carefully structured programme of early number work giving children a sound understanding of numbers, number patterns, money, measurement and basic mathematical vocabulary in preparation for key Stage 1.

Nursery Numbers Book 1 - 0 7217 0867 6

Nursery Numbers Book 2 - 0 7217 0868 4

Nursery Numbers Book 3 - 0 7217 0869 2

Nursery Numbers Book 4 - 0 7217 0870 6

Nursery Numbers Book 5 - 0 7217 0906 0

Nursery Numbers Book 6 - 0 7217 0907 9

Schofield & Sims pre-school products for 4+ year olds

Posters
Sturdy, laminated posters, full colour, write-on/wipe-off, suitable for wall mounting or desk top use. Over 70 titles including the alphabet, numbers, colours, days, shapes, nursery rhymes, opposites, seasons, time, weather and our bodies.

Information
For further information about products for pre-school, Key Stage 1 and 2, please request our catalogue or visit our website at
www.schofieldandsims.co.uk

Nursery workbooks
Nursery Land
Books 1 - 4
A brand new series of workbooks packed with activities based on popular nursery rhymes, to help develop basic concepts and skills. Includes dot-to-dot, numbers 1-10, colour, shape, size, matching and odd one out.

Nursery Activity
Books 1 - 6
This graded series of six activity books helps pre-school children apply their practical and oral skills to more concrete written work. Exercises cover a variety of pre-reading and early mathematical skills to help development of left and right co-ordination, sequencing, counting and number writing practice, shape and number recognition and colour recognition.

Nursery Writing
Books 1 - 6
A series of graded workbooks to aid the development of pre-reading and early writing skills, including left-to-right co-ordination, pencil control, visual perception, letter recognition, the alphabet, word recognition, and word writing. Fun-to-do exercises reinforce and develop skills and understanding.

Nursery All About
Books 1 - 4
Series consists of four books: All About Me, All About Where I Live, All About The World I Live In and All About The Weather. Each book is designed to develop young children's awareness of their environment, helping to sharpen their powers of observation and consolidate basic concepts and skills. Enthusiasm for learning is encouraged through fun activities, which give ample opportunity for parental support.

Author   Sally Johnson
Illustrator   Linzi Henry
Cover design   Curve Creative - Bradford

©2001 Schofield & Sims Ltd.

First printed 2001.

Printed by Hawthornes Printers, Nottingham

Schofield & Sims

Dogley Mill, Fenay Bridge, Huddersfield, HD8 0NQ
Phone 01484 607080   Fax 01484 606815

e-mail sales@schofieldandsims.co.uk

ISBN 0-7217-0869-2

9 780721 708690

Price £1.65
Pre-School
Age Range 4+ years